CUBES

by

BANX

Virgin Books

First published in Great Britain
in 1982 by Virgin Books Ltd,
95–99 Ladbroke Grove, London W11 1PG.

ISBN 0 907080 52 9

Printed in Great Britain by Nene Printing,
Sanders Road, Wellingborough, Northants.

Production services by Book Production
Consultants, Cambridge.

Colour separations and reproduction
by Capricorn Litho, Crescent Row,
London EC1.

Distributed by Hamlyn Paperbacks.

Jeremy Banks

Jeremy Banks has been a professional
cartoonist for nearly three years. He is a
regular contributor to Punch, Men Only and
The New Standard. This is his first book.

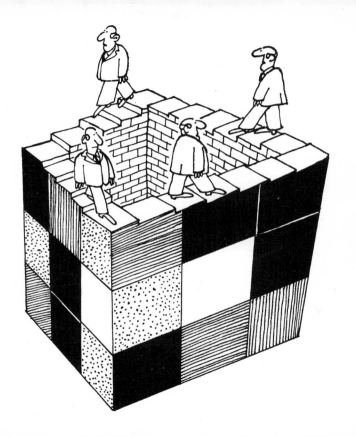

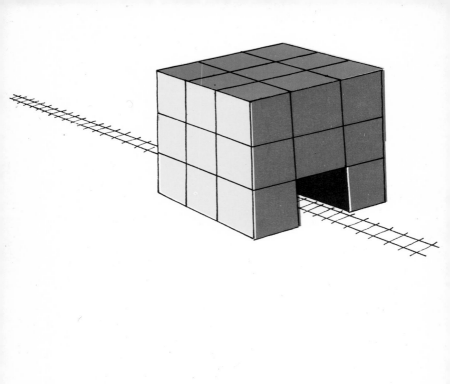

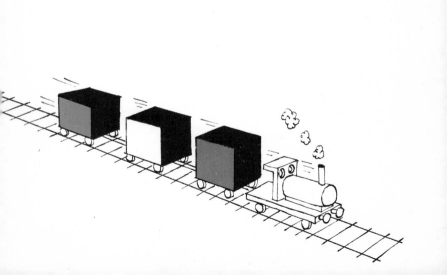

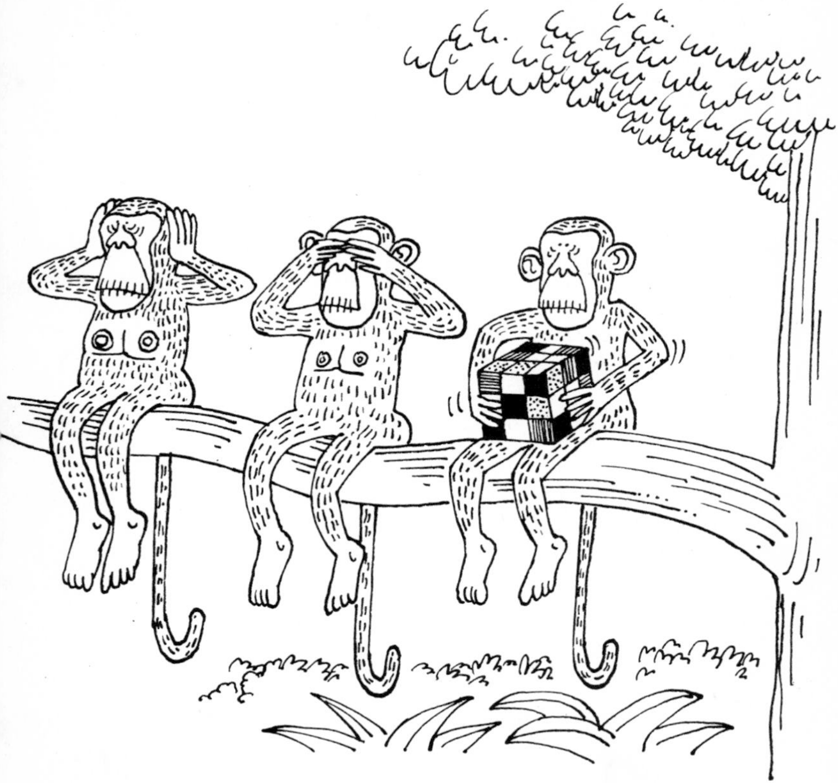

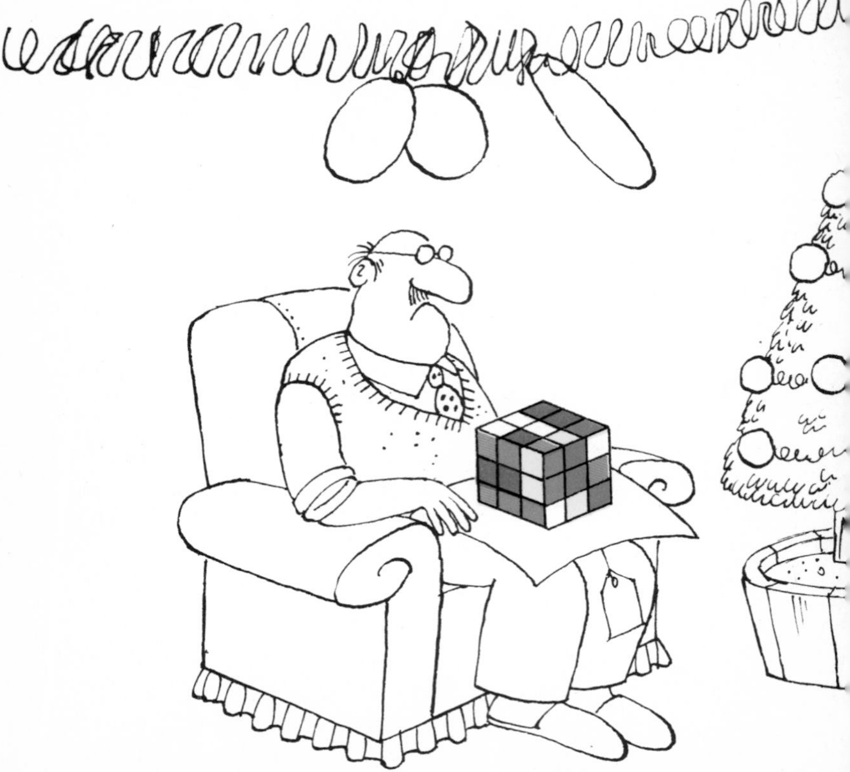

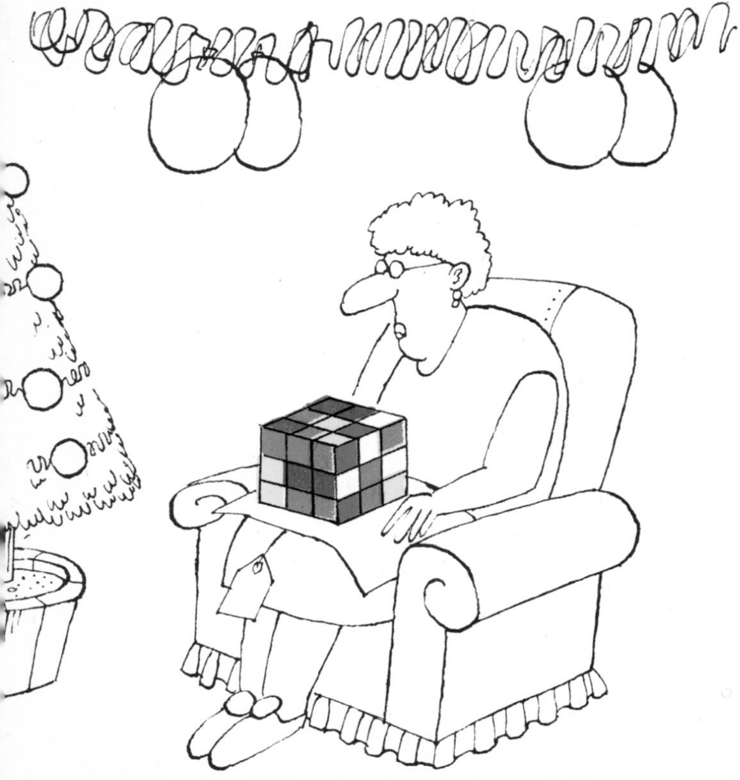

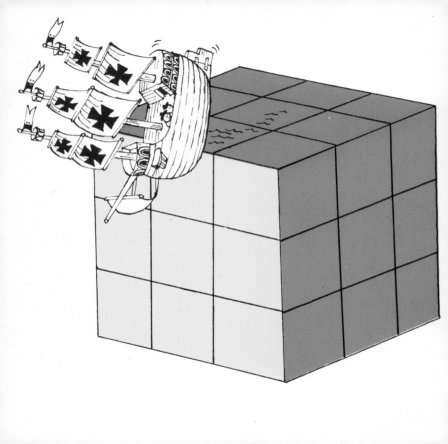

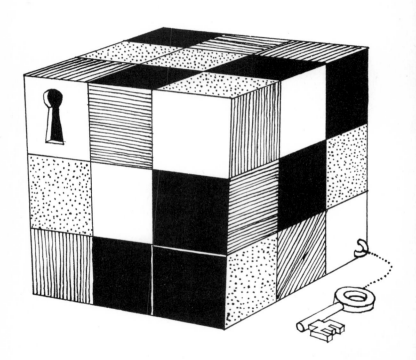

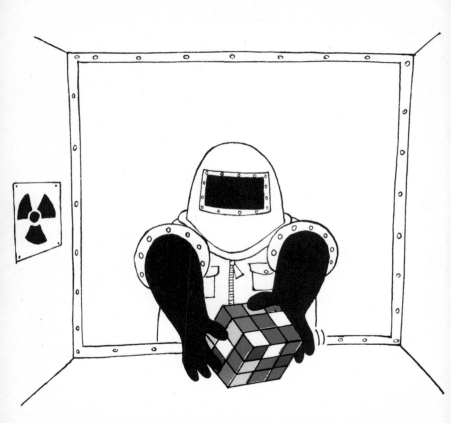

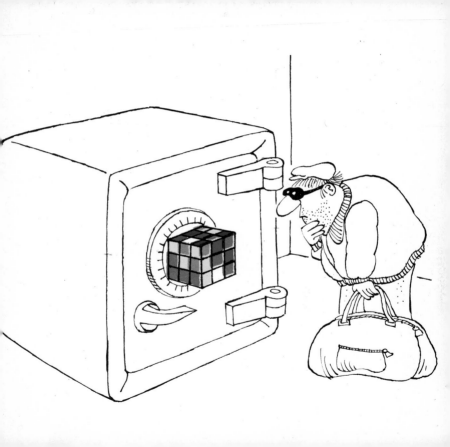

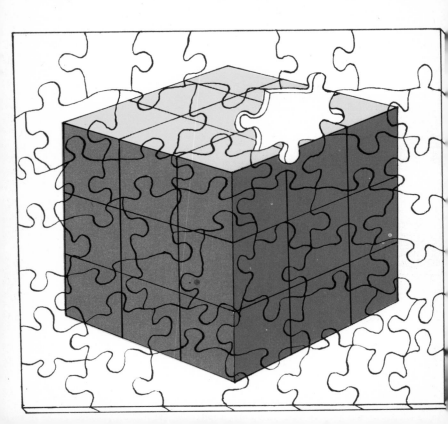

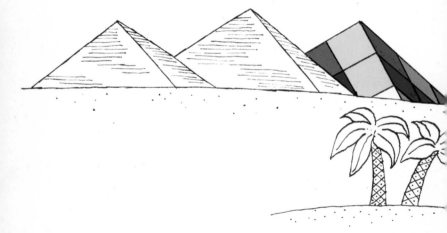

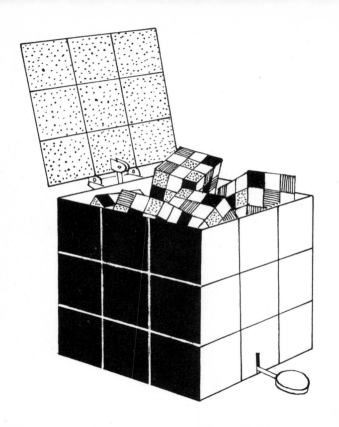

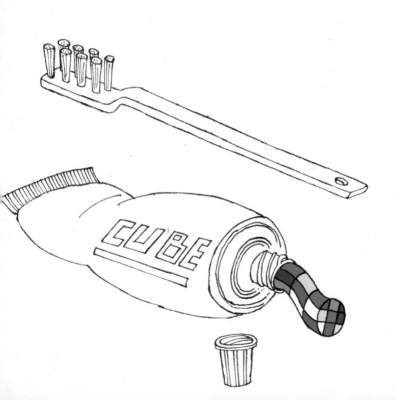

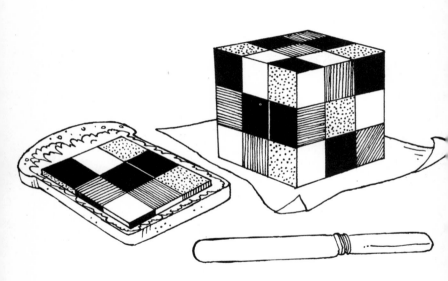

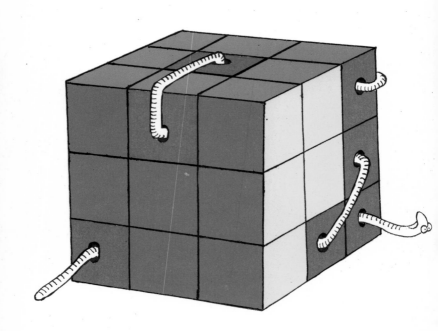

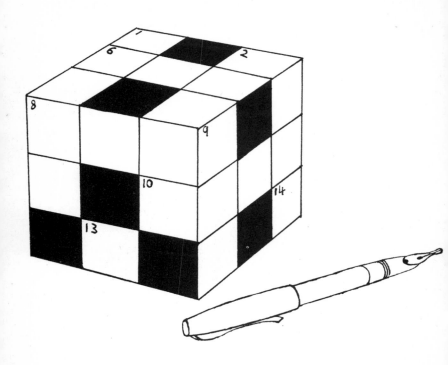

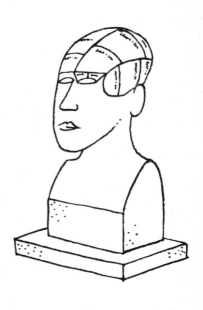

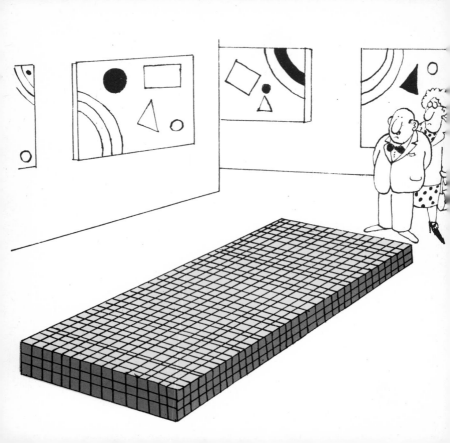

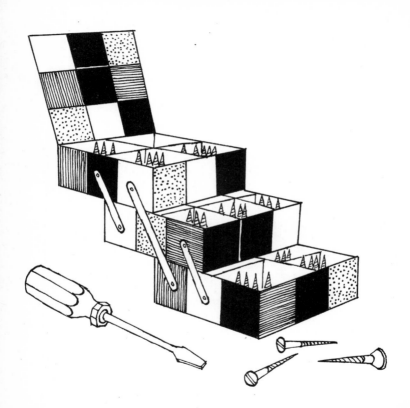

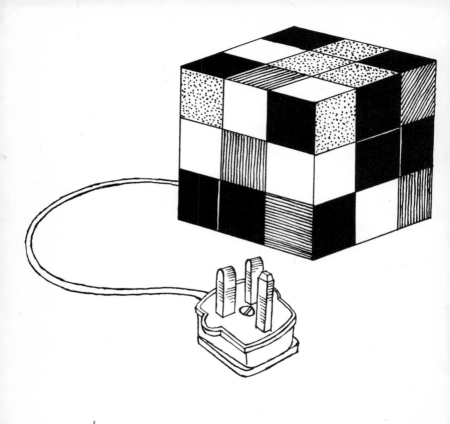

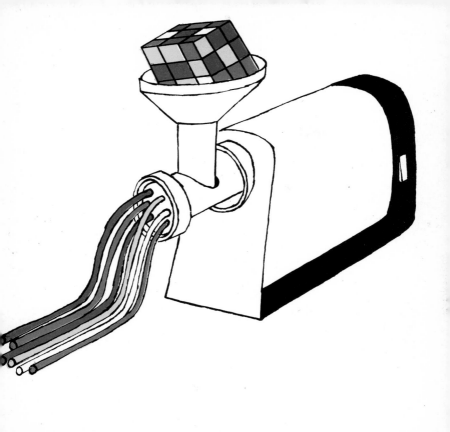

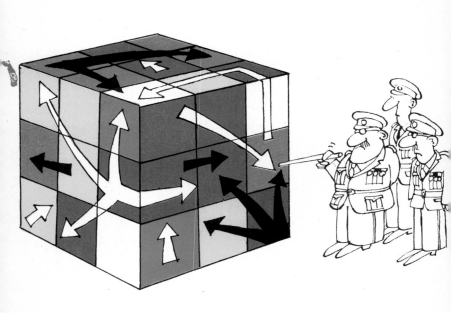

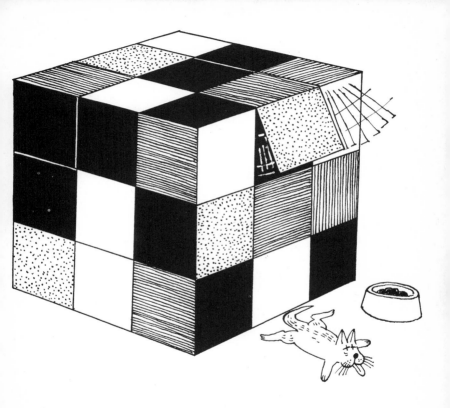

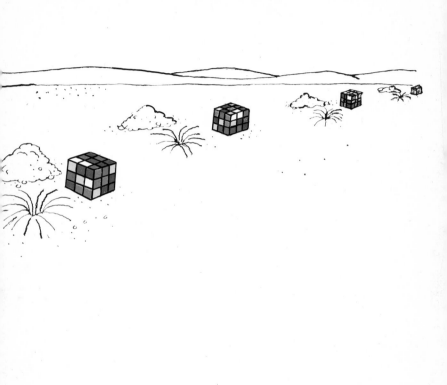